£3·99

80p

They're here to save the world! Those of you who have been following Marvel's **THE REAL GHOSTBUSTERS** comic, will be all too aware of the sort of beasties, ghosties and things that go bump in the night that our four heroes have already captured and contained. Those of you who are new to the busting business are in for a surprise or two. In this great second spook-slooping annual, **The Real Ghostbusters** pack their Proton Packs and head for Great Britain! So, if you're troubled by strange noises in the night, or you're experiencing weird feelings of dread, pick up a 'phone and ring **The Real Ghostbusters**!

CONTENTS

Cover by **ANDY LANNING**, **DAVE HARWOOD** and **JOHN BURNS**
Opening Spread by **BAMBOS** and **JOHN BURNS**
Editor **HELEN STONE** Assisted by **ANDY SEDDON** and **MIKE PHIPPS**
Spiritual Guide **DAN ABNETT**

THE REAL GHOST BUSTERS™

PETER VENKMAN

EGON SPENGLER

RAY STANTZ

WINSTON ZEDDMORE

JANINE MELNITZ

SLIMER

GHOSTBUSTERS: THE FACT BEHIND THE FANTASY!

by our roving reporter
CAL HACKER

SHOCK

The Real Ghostbusters: They're household names. Their exploits are internationally famous... We've got a lot to thank them for! But who are they? What is the hard-fact truth behind that dashing, devil-may-care exterior the public know and love. I had to get to the bottom of it, but as I took a cab downtown to their renowned HQ building, I had very little idea how I was going to do it. As we pulled up outside, and I got over my *shock* at size of the fare, I resolved to do my level best to get the truth, and that's what I got... that and whole lot more. I got the pain, the anger, the frustration, the preoccupation with a particular type of pizza. I got the *real* **Real Ghostbusters!**

HEARTBREAK

When I arrived, I found the Ghostbusters were already out on a bust. Their charming, hard-as-nails receptionist, Janine Melnitz, invited me to sit and wait for their return. Over a steamy cup of coffee, this dazzling, red-headed beauty told me about the tough hours her 'boys' worked, and told me about the anguish, the *heartbreak*, the downright soul-searing determination

they put into every bust. It was becoming clear to me then that any idea that busting was easy money was very, very wide of the mark indeed.

EXPOSED

After an hour or so, the Ghostbusters arrived home. Their powerful, roaring transport, ECTO-1, screamed in through the main portals like a Le Mans winner and spluttered to a halt. The four Ghostbusters climbed out, huddled and pinched with the cold. The bust had been on the top of a skyscraper in Manhattan, explained 'cuddly' Ray Stantz as the team tucked into a well-earned West Pier pizza, and it had been very, very cold up there.

Ray was worried that he might catch cold after being *exposed* to the elements in such a way.

HEART-THROB

"Hey, try some of this West Pier", cut in a voice, as Ray began to tell me about the way his mother darned his thermal underwear. "They've been really rampant with the chilli peppers!" The speaker was none other than the hunky Peter Venkman, debonair man-about-town, cool customer and professional heart-throb. "Got all that?" Peter asked chattily, as he took a seat next to me. "*Heart-throb* is hyphenated, I think." Well, we fell to talking like old friends, and in confidence, Peter disclosed to me the fundamental role he had played in all of the Ghostbusters' most crucial missions. Peter said that he wanted his true importance to go uncredited, and that praise should go to the team as a whole, but I can reveal here that it is good-looking six-footer Peter Venkman that puts the hero in Ghostbusters. I honestly felt as we sat there talking openly, sharing real and profound memories, that I was in the presence of true courage and strength.

Peter may blush when he reads this, but I have to say it. It's time that credit was given where credit is due. Peter Venkman, this American salutes you!

DANGEROUS

You can imagine how excited I was when I was invited to go on a bust with Winston Zeddemore and Egon Spengler, the duo who make up the Ghostbusters quartet. Winston was so keen for me to go with them, in fact, he almost dragged me physically away from Peter towards ECTO-1. After only five minutes turning her over, the speed-machine roared into life and we were away. As we headed for our target, I had to quicky stifle my fear at encountering the supernatural first hand. "This is Egon", Winston said, as he drove us hell-for-leather down the New York streets. "He's the brains behind the Ghostbusters." Egon seemed set in his seat with a look of grim determination as he held onto the baggage strap. "Hi", he whispered, as we lurched around another traffic island. Winston was undoubtedly proving to be the road demon of the team, driving the car so brilliantly that it all appeared so *dangerous* and out of control.

HACK

"When you write up your feature", Egon finally said as we pulled up at a set of lights, "I hope you're not going to be one of these *hacks* who lift a word at random from anything anybody says and set it up as a paragraph heading, thus utterly managing to distort the real meaning." "Gosh, me?", I replied, "no way!"

PLASTERED

Exactly what were we out to bust? 'Crucial' Winston Zeddemore was quick to explain. "It's not so much a bust, man", he reasoned, it's more that we're going to pick up some lost property." 'Brainy' Egon Spengler expanded on this. "We're looking for the sixth team member. He got left behind on the last bust. He's small, green and has a passion. . . no, a lust for food." I was intrigued. I was fascinated, and within three minutes of our arrival, I was *plastered* in green slime.

VIOLENT

Slimer, a Class five, full-roaming vapour, is the Ghostbusters' very own pet ghost, and he's the most

charming-a-friendly dead person this reporter has ever met. Though Winston warned me that most people develop a violent dislike for him, I warmed to his enthusiastic embrace, and we were soon talking like old friends. "Foody-foody yum-yum?" he asked me. "Back at basey-wasey", I assured him.

COURAGE

Overall, my abiding impression is one of a dedicated family of hard-working experts, prepared to dash out at the call of duty like a streak of light, to put aside their personal problems, anxieties and difficulties in order to get the job done, and then be prepared to accept no cre-dit whatsoever for the immense *courage* they have shown. These four men, one woman and one green thing, are a shining example of what makes this country great, and I feel privileged to have learned first-hand the brave self-denial behind the glamorous myth.

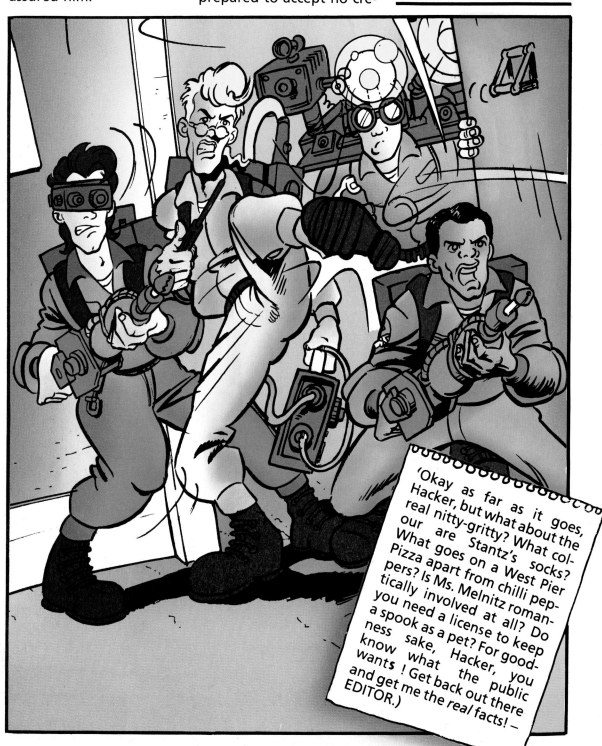

'Okay as far as it goes, Hacker, but what about the real nitty-gritty? What colour are Stantz's socks? What goes on a West Pier Pizza apart from chilli peppers? Is Ms. Melnitz romantically involved at all? Do you need a license to keep a spook as a pet? For goodness sake, Hacker, you know what the public wants! Get back out there and get me the real facts! – EDITOR.)

Story **JOHN CARNELL** ⊘ Art **ANTHONY LARCOMBE** ⊘ Lettering **GLIB** ⊘ Colouring **STEVE WHITE**

THE DEXTER'S CHAIN-STORE MASSACRE!

Donna Lacey was tired. Neck-achingly, eye-stingingly, 'Oh please let this film end and let me get to bed'-ingly tired. However, the slim, attractive, blonde-haired Donna wasn't at home in front of the TV, she was working overtime, dressing the dummies in the fashion window display of Dexter's Superstore in Manhattan's brand new Barndale Shopping Centre.

The mall was to be officially opened the next day, but earlier, the press and TV people had been shown around, and one had turned his nose up at the Dexter fashion display. Hardly a chorus of disapproval, but it was discovered that this dissenter's surname was Dexter. Panic gripped the powers-that-be at the Superstore, giving rise to Donna's third consecutive 16-hour day.

Now, she was alone in the mall, too tired to care that, in fact, the media man, Dexter was no connection whatsoever to his namesakes who owned a string of shops across America. She was also too tired to worry about the faint rhythmic tapping sound that had started a few minutes earlier and seemed to be coming from somewhere beneath her feet. Even when she saw one of the shop dummies turn its head towards her, Donna dismissed it, convinced that her exhausted mind was playing tricks on her.

When the same mannequin moved its arm and took its first step forward, she was forced to reassess the situation. Slowly and silently, another shop dummy turned its head to look at Donna. A third followed suit. Exhausted or not, Donna's mind began screaming at her to get the heck out of there.

The stilted steps of the first dummy took it straight through the plate glass window. Donna darted out after it, aware that the remaining mannequins in the display were also putting their best plastic feet forward. An instant later though, Donna was falling. Had it been her fault? Had she run into the heel of the first dummy? Or had he – it! *IT,* she scolded herself – left the heel there to trip her over? Whatever the reason, she hit the ground hard. Lying there, trying to catch her breath, Donna was aware of more glass smashing. She glanced up to see mannequins breaking out of other shops in the mall, taking rigid, straight-legged strides towards her.

Donna struggled to her feet. She wanted to run, but ahead, behind, to her left and right, zombie-like dummies were closing in. She could see no escape. The mannequins shuffled forward, forming a circle with the frightened Donna at its centre. On they came, tightening the circle with every staccato step. Plastic hands and fingers reached out, flexed to grab her. Finally they found her, and Donna screamed.

It was the longest, loudest scream she had ever made, but at the end of it, Donna was still surrounded by a dozen or so dummies. Their hands and fingers however, were mercifully still. The dummies had become devoid of life once more – lifeless and unthreatening. Donna pushed several over to confirm this as she escaped the circle. It was over and she suddenly felt more tired than ever. Nevertheless, despite the drowsiness she knew who she had to call .

"Wow!" said Ray Stantz, as the Ghostbusters charged into the mall and saw the destruction. Glass was everywhere – there was hardly a shop window left intact – and packed into the avenues was the army of dummies.

"Not your usual crowd of late-night shoppers". added Peter Venkman as the quartet threaded their way through the plastic men and women towards

Story **IAN RIMMER** ⊘ Art **MARTIN GRIFFITHS** ⊘ Colouring **STUART PLACE**

the anxious Donna Lacey.

"That's what I call service!" the relieved window-dresser began. "I only called you a couple of minutes ago."

"Fortunately we were just passing, returning from another job, when your call came through", said Winston Zeddmore. "And what a call! Mannequins on the march!"

"Yes" replied Donna, self-consciously. "Sounds unbelievable, huh?"

Winston smiled. "Lady, we see some weird stuff everyday, but I still don't believe ninety percent of it myself!"

"Wow – is that true, Winston?" asked Ray.

Peter looked quizzically at Ray, whom he suspected believed one hundred and ten per cent of everything he saw. Something about Ray was bothering Peter, but at that second he just couldn't pin it down.

"Wow, guys! Can you –" began Ray, but he got no further because Peter loudly interrupted him. This was a pity, for what Ray was about to say would have had a great bearing upon the case. To be fair to Peter,

he had no way of knowing this, and seeing as he had just realised what it was about Ray that was bothering him, he felt fully justified in interrupting.

"Got it!" he yelled, turning to Ray. "It's the way you keep saying 'Wow!' all the time. It's bugging the heck out of me!"

"Wow!" said Winston suddenly.

"Don't you start!" warned Peter. Then he saw the look in Winston's eyes, and followed his gaze to a mannequin. It was moving again.

"Still no PKE", Egon called out as Donna and the others began to edge away from the shop dummies. They were coming to life again and discovering that they could move as fluidly as any Frankenstein's Monster. In no time at all, the five were backed up against Dexter's Superstore.

"We need to open fire or move inside", urged Winston.

"What we need," corrected Peter, "is an Ectoplasmic Pied Piper to come and lead these creeps away!"

"Er, just in case he

doesn't pop by", Donna said, already stepping back through the shattered window in Dexter's, "how about if we take refuge?"

Donna's suggestion met with approval and shortly after, the Ghostbusters lined up in Dexter's food hall. They faced the fashion display window, Proton Guns at the ready. "The narrow opening will slow down any dummies which follow us", reassured Egon, "and we can use the Ecto-Splat to hold them off if necessary."

When the sixth mannequin in as many seconds shuffled into the department store, it was necessary. The five crouched in a kneeling position and fired a volley of proton ions from their weapons. Beams of light energy cracked and sparked above the shop floor and four dummies exploded into little pieces of smouldering plastic. However, a dozen more synthetic zombies were already crowding into the store.

"Can't take a hint, can they?" Peter said. "Okay, let's hit 'em again – harder!" He raised his Proton Gun to fire again, leaning a shoulder against a chest of frozen food to brace himself. Unfortunately, it was food in this fridge that first discovered that it too could move.

Dexter's food hall became a battleground. Tomatoes, far from rotten, began to pelt Donna and Winston. Egon fell victim to a combined attack from the fish and confectionary departments which was both smelly and fattening by turns. Several salami sausages began clubbing Ray, forcing him to yell out,

"Wow – oww! Wow – oww!" repeatedly.

The dairy products concentrated on Peter. Cartons of cream – single, double and whipped – unloaded their contents over him. Pots of yoghurt, coleslaw and cream cheese joined the attack, supporting the 'heavy artillery' of a family-sized strawberry mousse and two black forest gateaux. "What is it with gooey, splatty gunk and me?" Peter hollered despairingly.

The hard stuff – tinned fruit and frozen cuts of meat – bombarded the mannequins, which were reeling under the onslaught as much as the Ghostbusters. "Glory be, when is this madness going to end", cried Donna Lacey. Just then, it did.

"There's something fishy here, besides myself", Egon finally surmised. "Some cyclical force within the mall is bringing normally inanimate objects to life. Its effect seems to be cumulative, so we have to discover the source before it begins

again – in approximately eight minutes."

"Or we'll be in serious trifle here", added the dripping, creamy mess that was once Peter Venkman.

Donna led the Ghostbusters out of Dexter's to a map of the mall The five stared hard at it, but saw nothing that gave any clues to the whereabouts of Egon's 'cyclical force'. "Five minutes to the next activity", Egon warned gravely.

Then Winston spotted something on the basement section of the map. One of the shop names was printed on a sticky label, covering a space which had originally been assigned to a different shop. "It's a longshot", Winston sighed, "but let's take a look."

Holding his breath, Ray prized the last of the sticker clear, then gasped, "Wow – oops, sorry Peter", at the name that was revealed. It said Little Shoppe II.

Having sent Donna out of the mall for safety, the phantom-fighting foursome raced down to the basement. "It's falling into place", shouted Egon as they ran. "We know the Shoppe Keeper is a nasty piece of work after we caught him selling Ghost-Transference Objects from his original Shoppe. He seemed to sell just about everything from that weird place, only people were getting a lot more than they bargained for."

"I thought we'd seen the last of that evil dealer", added Winston. "Guess it's lucky the authorities here stopped him setting up Shoppe again."

"Yeah, but he's obviously rigged up something in the mal to take revenge", said Peter, squelching along be-

hind. "The question is what?"

The site that the Little Shoppe II would have occupied was directly below Dexter's Superstore. The replacement shop was an electrical goods store, but when the four found it, only Peter saw anything unusual.

"A Vunkman Quadrophonic Fully-Programmable Reel-To-Reel Tape Recorder", he enthused, pointing out a piece of equipment at the back of the store with a banana yoghurt-flavoured finger. "I know all about Vunkman equipment because the name has a certain ring to it. I knew they were bringing out this little baby, but it's the first one I've seen. Look at the smooth action as it rewinds its tape . . ."

"Rewinds?" queried Egon, thoughtfully.

"Yeah. See it's been programmed to – oh, hold it. It's switched to play. Guess it's a loop programme – play, rewind, play, and so on."

For the third time that night, a strange rhythmic tapping sound began to filter out of the shop. "Wow, guys. That's the noise . . ." began Ray.

"Ray, you're still doing it!" interrupted Peter irritably.

" . . . that I tried to point out earlier, before being interrupted by Dessert Man here!" Ray doggedly persisted.

Four pennies dropped simultaneously, and four Proton Guns were quickly pointed at the Vunkman tape machine – four-tenths of a second too late. The inanimate activity had begun an instant earlier and before the 'busters could

fire, they were bombed with balls. American footballs, squash balls, softball balls and tennis balls from a nearby sports shop, plus aniseed balls from the sweet shop opposite. Under the bouncing barrage, the four lost their aim. Winston took a heavy hit from a medicine ball and was sent toppling. He landed facing a toy shop, out of which he saw a troop of teddy bears marching purposefully behind a miniature, mechanical model of . . . Mr Stay-Puft, the Marshmallow Man!

"Oh no! Not him again!" fumed Winston. He opened fire with a full charge of Ecto-Splat at the waddling, sickly cute figure. When he finally relaxed his trigger finger, Mr Stay-Puft was nowhere to be seen. "That got rid of him!" thought Winston triumphantly and, as it happened, quite incorrectly.

Near by, Egon was being pelted with perfume bottles, several of which hit and exploded on the surrounding walls. "Somedays", he complained bitterly, "this job really stinks!"

Ray and Peter were being buzzed by books and pieces of crockery.

"Wow – it's only just begun and already the activity is much worse than before", said Ray.

"Guys", called Egon, as several vacuum cleaners hoovered straight out of the electrical goods shop window, "I think I know what weapon we need to deal with a situation like this."

"Then why aren't we using it?" Peter asked impatiently.

"Well, I haven't actually invented it yet", Egon replied.

"Until you do, this is hopeless", yelled Winston, who suddenly felt something tugging at his trouser-leg. He glanced down and saw the smoking, charred, but unmistakeable form of the Mr Stay-Puft toy wrapping itself around his ankle.

"Arrrgh!" howled Winston, kicking out at the smoke-blackened, bloated body. In doing so, he lost his footing and tumbled backwards through the broken electrical goods shop window. With arms

flailing, one outstretched hand caught in some cables close to the wall and yanked something free. Instantly, everything stopped.

Winston glanced to the wall and noted that he'd pulled a plug out of an electrical socket. He didn't need to trace the cable all the way to the Vunkman tape machine to realise what had happened. Instead, he reached forward, lifted the now lifeless Mr Stay-Puft toy off his ankle, and grinned. "So you finally teamed up with the good guys, huh?" he said.

"'Great . .?" suggested Ray, as the four walked out of the mall. Beneath the cream and gateau, Peter pulled a face.

"Okay, what about 'Golly' or 'Grief' . .?"

"Try another letter", Peter instructed.

Ray looked up from the dictionary. "Tough break on the souvenir front", he said. "I mean, Egon's got the tape from the machine – which the Shoppe Keeper must have programmed during the press preview – to analyse and study. Who knows, maybe we'll pick up some leads from it and finally track down that creep. Anyway, Egon has the tape, Winston's hanging on to the Mr Stay-Puft toy of course, and I've got this dictionary, but er, you don't seem to have anything, Peter."

Peter turned to Ray and winked as Donna Lacey rushed up to them. She took a handkerchief and gently wiped Peter's face clean of dairy products. "My hero", she sighed and placed a grateful kiss full on his lips.

"Wow . . ." said Peter.

THE REAL GHOSTBUSTERS

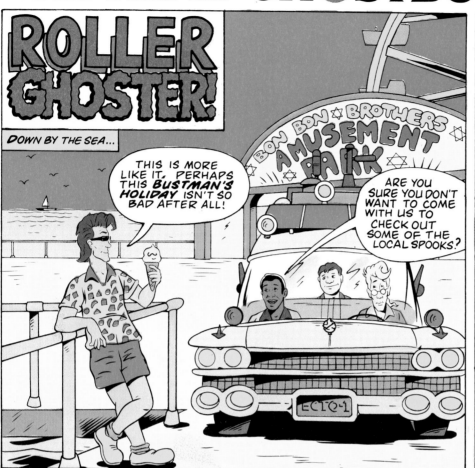

Story **JOHN CARNELL** ⊘ Art **BRIAN WILLIAMSON** and **DAVE HARWOOD** ⊘ Lettering **HEL** ⊘ Colouring **LYNN WHIT**

CLASSIFICATION OF SPOOKS

CLASSIFICATION	APPEARANCE	SYMPTOMS
CLASS ONE	A vapour, mist or other non-manifested haunting.	Strange smells, spectral lights, odd noises like a sack of spanners falling into a trifle.
CLASS TWO	Semi-focused, partial phantoms such as animated skulls, mouths hands or poltergeists.	Nasty odours, power cuts, sudden drops in temperature, moving crockery, strange feelings of dread.
CLASS THREE	Non-specific past-life repeaters such as full-torso apparitions, zombies or ghouls.	Overwhelming sense of terror, glowing manifestations, general foul stenches.

WHAT YOU SEE

TACTICS

Straight forward PKE detection and entrapment.

Spectro-goggles necessary to detect spook. Selective protonic entrapment with one or two Proton Guns.

Trained Proton Gunners only. Usually two or more needed. Peg for nose.

CLASSIFICATION	APPEARANCE	SYMPTOMS
CLASS FOUR	Specific past-life repeaters such as ghosts of historical figures or ghosts that communicate and have discernible personalities.	Fully-formed apparitions, cold, clinging fear, spectral voices and unusually horrible reeks.
CLASS FIVE	Focused, non-terminal repeating, full-floating, free-roaming phantasms. Any non-human spook such as Slimer.	Paranormal chaos and general Psycho-kinetic disturbance. Ectoplasmic residue in large quantities. Extremely bad smells.
CLASS SIX	Major free-roaming phantasms such as the Stay-Puft Marshmallow Man, or any demonic Servitor of a similar type.	Major population centres in jeopardy, tidal waves, drought, sudden eclipses of the moon and sun, unbelievably bad smells.
CLASS SEVEN	Metaspectres, major demonic deities such as Gozer, Zuul, Ponquadragor, Quelztalcum etc.	Plague, terror, mass hysteria, cats and dogs living together, the end of the World. Also nasty smells.

Research required to detect weaknesses. Two or three experienced Proton Gunners. Gas mask optional.

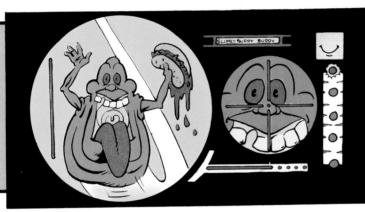

Hold your breath and wear wash and wear clothing. Three to four expert Gunners needed to form a three or four beam ionic cross to lock and trap spook.

Be on holiday abroad. Failing that, try crossing the ionic streams and hope the overload causes a Total Protonic Reversal Not to be attempted by amateurs or anyone sane.

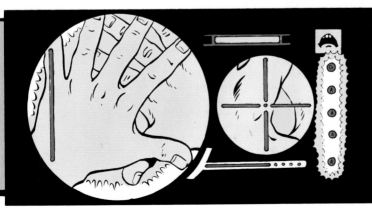

Tell yourself "Busting makes me feel good" and try anything! After that, further tactics include running away or taking up a safer job like lion taming or absailing down The Eiger without a rope.

Story RICHARD ALAN ⊘ **Art ANTHONY WILLIAMS** ⊘ **Colouring STEVE WHITE**

THE GREEN GHOSTS!

Joe Sheen worked for Avelco Plastics in Poughkeepsie, New York state, USA. He was the night watchman at the factory there, and he was very good at his job. Every evening at five-thirty precisely, Joe would clock in just before it was time for all the employees to leave. Joe was a loner, that was why he enjoyed his night-time job at the factory. Once everyone else had gone home, Joe and the two Alsatian guard dogs – Rex and Samson – had the entire place to themselves and that was the way Joe liked it. He was getting on in his years (although he was still as tough as an old boot) and so the hustle and bustle of a nine-to-five daytime job had lost its appeal to him a long time ago. No, sometimes the Plastics factory was a pretty eerie place to be at night, but nothing spooky had ever happened to him in the three years he'd been working there.

Not until this particular night.

Joe had locked up as usual at seven o'clock sharp. He fed Rex and Samson at seven-ten and then began his rounds with them at approximately seven-twenty.

The factory floor at Avelco Plastics was filled by six

giant vats of bubbling plastics. Tubes led in and out of the vats, carrying raw materials from one to another. The whole set up at the factory reminded Joe of a horror film he saw many many years ago but it hadn't frightened him and he'd never gone

to see another horror film again. Nothing ever frightened Joe.

Not until this particular night.

You see, Joe was walking the dogs down the aisle between the two sets of vats when he suddenly heard a Strange Noise. It was very much like the sound of a girl crying. As he got closer to the far end of the factory floor, the crying got louder. In fact, it now seemed as if there was more than just one girl crying – it sounded as if there were several. Joe was a softy at heart, and he would always comfort people in times of distress, but these sniffling, sobbing noises sent a shiver down his spine. He noticed that the sounds were coming from the massive drainage pipe that collected all the waste products from the factory. So, as he approached the pipe, he quietly and, as calmly as he could, slipped the collars off Rex and Samson. The dogs needed no further instruction. The two of them bounded away from Joe and towards the source of the Strange Noises. For a few moments the dogs disappeared into the shadows at the end of the factory and all Joe could hear was the sound of them barking inquisitively and the sound of people sobbing. Then, all the noises stopped simultaneously and another shiver ran down Joe's spine. The seconds that passed during that time seemed like hours to Joe. He stood frozen to the spot, not knowing what to do. Then, like two bats out of hell, Rex and Samson came tearing out of the darkness back towards him. Their faces were masks of abject terror and they were yelping in a manner that Joe found most unnerving. There were three, no four, no – five or six vaporous apparitions. They were a sickly green colour and they came screaming out of the

shadows at Joe before he had time to think. They whirled around him, wailing and howling, and for a moment, Joe thought he heard one of them say "Leave, leave, you are killing us!" It was at that moment that Joe summoned up every joule of energy in his body, turned tail and ran. There was only one other thing he did before he left the factory lot completely. He made a 'phonecall.

When the Ghostbusters arrived at the Plastics factory, the place was floodlit and swarming with police, newsmen and photographers. Joe hadn't rung the Ghostbusters direct. He'd rung his boss, the manager of the factory, Mr Sloman. Sloman had rung the police, someone at the police station had leaked the story to the newspapers and someone on one of the newspapers had, quite sensibly, made a call to Ghostbusters' Headquarters. It was approaching midnight when Egon answered the call but, even so, the four Ghostbusters readied themselves for action immediately. Well, Egon, Ray and Winston readied themselves for action. Peter, who claimed he'd already had a really hard day, simply rolled out of bed and climbed wearily into the back of ECTO-1 without even bothering to change out of the T-shirt and jockey shorts that he usually slept in. The others were too eager to answer the call to wait for him to change, so they all piled into ECTO-1 after him and, with Ray at the wheel, drove as fast as they could to Poughkeepsie.

"Say, what's going on,

Inspector?" asked Winston as he walked up to the police cordon, outside the factory gates. "Ghostbusters, thank goodness you're here!" said the police inspector, with a genuine note of gratitude in his voice. He'd been on the case for almost an hour now, and he'd realised in the first five minutes that it was way beyond his comprehension. Quickly, and concisely, he told the Ghostbusters everything that he knew about Joe Sheen's experience earlier in the evening.

"Where's Joe now?" asked Ray when the inspector had finished. "If we're going to go in there, we'll need someone who knows their way around."

At that moment, a short, balding man with a very worried expression on his face stepped forward. "Joe's gone home to calm down", he said. "But I'm the manager of the factory, and I'd be glad to take you in there. I want those ghosts out of there right away!"

"Okay", said Peter, yawning, "but be sure to bring your cheque book with you, we don't get up in the middle of the night for nothing you know."

"Are you *with* the Ghostbusters?" said Sloman, looking suspiciously at Peter, who was still dressed in his 'Metal Witch' T-shirt and heart-patterned jockey shorts.

"Hey, listen, man", said Peter crossly, "this is a new costume that I'm modelling especially for this occasion. If it catches on, could be we'll ALL go out on busts in this kind of get up."

Egon raised an eyebrow at this last remark, but chose not to comment. He simply handed Peter his Proton Pack and Proton Gun and the four Ghostbusters and their guide made their way into the factory.

"WOW", said Peter. Then he said it again. "WOW!"

The green ghosts were everywhere — there were about twenty or thirty of them now. They all appeared to be female and all were flying round the plastic vats wailing and screaming and generally making lots of Very Unpleasant and STRANGE Noises.

"WOW", said Peter for a third and final time.

"Okay", shouted Egon above the cacophony of screams and howls, "Looks like we've got a hard day's night ahead of us. Let's start busting! Heat 'em up!"

"Smoking!" chorused the others.

"Let 'em rip!" shouted Peter jubilantly.

The Proton Cannon's hum began to build up, and with Sloman cowering behind them, the Ghostbusters started doing what they do best — busting ghosts! For half an hour the factory was lit by the vaporous green light cast by the ghosts and the bright blue and yellow light cast by the Ghostbuster's Proton Guns. At the end of that half an hour, Ghost Traps littered the floor at the Ghostbusters feet and you might have thought that the job was done, but it wasn't. At the end of that half an hour, there were still as many ghosts in the factory, wailing and screaming, as there were when the 'busters had walked in.

"I don't understand it", shouted Ray to Egon over the noise, "it seems that no matter how many of these things we zap, there's still more of them manifesting every minute! Could they be self-multiplying apparitions?"

"I don't know, Ray", said Egon. "I think we should switch off our Proton Packs and completely reassess this situation."

So they switched off their Packs and, when the hum of the cannons had died down, Egon turned to address the others. "It seems to me", he said, "that the source of these strange, green manifestations is situated at the back of the factory floor. Mr Sloman, would you kindly lead us over there?"

"What?" said Sloman, who was quaking visibly and hoping that everybody had forgotten him. "You want me to walk through that lot?" Sloman pointed up at the vaporous green mass of ghosts that were still wailing and screaming around the plastics vats.

"Mr Sloman, it is my considered opinion that these ghosts are not likely to harm you whilst you are in our company. They have witnessed our ability to trap them and so it is unlikely that they will attack us while we are still armed. Please, lead the way."

It took five minutes to get to the back of the factory. However, as they reached the drainage pipe at the back of the factory, they had to hold back. The pipe glowed green in the dark and it was becoming quite clear that the ghosts were emerging into the factory from the pipe.

"Sloman, where does that pipe lead?" asked Egon thoughtfully.

"Well, it's the drainage pipe. It collects all the by-products created by the plastic-manufacturing process and, well, it, er . . ."

"It what ..?" asked Winston firmly.

"Well, it, er . . . it disposes of them", said Sloman meekly.

"I see", said Egon knowingly. "I think I'm beginning to understand this situation a bit more clearly. Tell me, Mr Sloman, is there a way of getting out of the back of the factory?"

When the Ghostbusters got outside they saw that the drainage pipe led away from the factory, stretched out across a vacant lot and

then dipped down . . . over the bank of a river. Egon led the rest of the team over to the river. "No wonder this factory is haunted", he commented sadly. "Look . . ."

They didn't like what they saw. The drainage pipe was pumping a thick black substance out of its mouth and into the river. Dead fish floated on the water's surface. The riverbanks were grey and totally stripped of vegetation. As far as the eye could see, everything natural was either dead or dying. It was the middle of summer, but over a hundred yards away from the drainage pipe, a tree stood with not a leaf to be seen on its branches. It seemed to be leaning to one side like a sick old man.

Winston found himself gagging. "Man, this place just SMELLS of death", he said, turning away. The others just stared on in horror.

It was Egon that broke the silence. "Mr Sloman, I'm afraid that there is little more we can do for you here. Whilst you continue to pollute the countryside in this horrible fashion, your factory will continue to be haunted."

"But-but, you're Ghostbusters! I'm paying for your time – you *have* to help me!" Sloman managed to sound indignant, but his embarrassment and guilt were written all over his face.

Ray prodded a finger at Sloman, angrily. "Mr Sloman, you are being haunted by the vaporous manifestations of river nymphs, tree nymphs and the spirits of the countryside. You are being haunted by Mother Nature herself! You have to help *yourself!*" Ray turned away, beckoning to the others. "C'mon, you lot. Let's write this one off as a bad job. I wouldn't *want* to take this man's money!"

As Winston and Peter followed Ray out, Egon stopped by Sloman for a minute. "Mr Sloman, I can see that you're not a bad man, and you could still lift the curse that has been placed on your factory quite easily. You don't have to treat the by-products of your plastics operation as waste. Stop pumping this stuff into the river and have your scientists examine its composition and I'm sure you'll find that you'll be able to find a way to develop the subst-

ance into something useful. All it will take is a bit of investment of your time and money. In the meantime, spend the money that you were prepared to pay us, and rectify the wrongs that you've wrought on your environment here. In good time, you'll find that the hauntings will stop and your factory will be able to get back to work."

EPILOGUE

Sloman took Egon's advice. He stopped pumping the waste products into the river and closed down his factory until his scientists were able to develop a process whereby the substances could be recycled. After many months of work, Sloman's men had come up with a solution. After some time, they were successful and Sloman wasted no time before putting his product into practice. He transformed the vacant lot into an enormous greenhouse – and each pane of glass was not, in fact, glass, but a by-product of Avelco Plastics. Sloman was soon able to restore life to the countryside and the ghosts disappeared.

THE REAL GHOSTBUSTERS™

'PHONE PHANTOM!

GHOSTBUSTERS' HQ...

RING RING

HELLO, GHOSTBUSTERS! YES, OF COURSE WE'RE SERIOUS! HOW CAN I...

WE'VE GOT FOURTEEN HEADLESS HORSEMEN OUT HERE, YOU HAVE TO —

RING RING

HANG ON, THERE'S SOMEONE ON THE OTHER LINE...

GHOSTBUSTERS, CAN I HELP YOU —?

IT'S THE APOCALYPSE! SEND YOUR MEN RIGHT AWAY!

RING RING

THERE ARE TEN STAY-PUFT MONSTERS AT LARGE IN NEW YORK...

THE END OF THE WORLD CAN WAIT! I'VE HAD IT!

...TWENTY VAPOROUS APPARITIONS!

SOMETHING'S VERY WRONG HERE! THOSE 'PHONES HAVEN'T STOPPED RINGING!

GREMLINS EVERYWHERE!

VAMPIRES! WEREWOLVES!

HEY, WAIT A MINUTE! WHAT'S THIS?!

JUNCTION BOX

YOU'VE GOT TO HELP... HEE! HEE! HEE!

FOURTEEN SLIMERS... HEE! HEE! HEE!

Hee! Hee! THEN I NEED SOME HELP WITH SOME FLYING SAUCERS... Hee! He — OOPS!

NOBODY MESSES WITH MY 'PHONES YOU LINE-CROSSING CREEP! OUT!

THIS'LL TEACH YOU TO TANGLE YOUR WIRES WITH JANINE MELNITZ...

YES, SIR... I'LL TAKE A MESSAGE! RIGHT AWAY, SIR!

'CAUSE WHEN IT COMES TO DEALING WITH 'PHONEY PHANTOMS, I'M A COOL OPERATOR!

Story JOHN CARNELL ⦸ Art ANTHONY LARCOMBE ⦸ Lettering and Colouring ZED

SPENGLER'S SPIRIT GUIDE

This Spirit Guide is, of course, the most thorough and up-to-date available, but I thought you might find it useful if I took this opportunity to assess the other works of similar content available.

SPENGLER'S GOOD SPOOK GUIDE GUIDE

THE BLACK TOME OF ANTIOCH
Only available through mail order in a braile edition. Deals mainly with the Pointy-toothed class fours. Wear gloves when looking at the diagrams.
Rating ★★.

McCAVITY'S WEE VOLUME
Vividly written but, essentially about as much use as a purple kipper. A few good jokes, like the one about the ghoul and the electric tooth brush, but little else.
Rating –.

NOGGAHEIM'S ENORMOUSLY VAST BOOK OF GHOSTS
Absolutely useless, but big enough to stun a rhino if swung hard enough. Less a work of academic research than an offensive weapon.
Rating ★.

SCOBB'S GUIDE
Terse. Good. Doesn't say much.
Rating ★.

THE MERONICAMONO-COMON
Written in Urdu in invisible ink. Only buy it if you are very very patient.
Rating

STAR'S COMPENDIUM OF THE PARANORMAL
Very basic and, as it is badly translated from the Serbo-Croat, very misleading. For instance, Chapter Three.
"... if you meet a class six Servitor, do stick your head in its mouth and invite him to bite it off ..." This should, of course, read "... don't!" Rating ★.

SCRORNHIDE'S BIGGE BOOKE OF BUGGABOOS
Pretty influential work of the late 14th Century, which led to everything being called a Buggaboo. This of course led to problems such as it being impossible to tell if he was talking about a ghostly knocking or a whole plague of class six phantoms. Misleading.
Rating ★.

WHICH WITCH?
Cheap attempt by the *Consumer Association* to jump on the band wagon and get a few cheap laughs at the same time. Paperback.
Rating –.

BRAYNECHILDE'S VARORIUM
The work of a fruitcake which should be avoided like the plague. Not even nicely bound. Rating –.

TOBIN'S SPIRIT GUIDE
About the best of the rest. Thorough, informative, but a little out of date as it was written in the year 327 AD. Difficult to obtain.
Rating ★★★.

YILONGATHROK'S MOGAHEDARON
This is either a Spirit Guide or a road atlas of pre-Christian Mesopotamia. Anyone out there read Cunniform?
Rating ?

THE REAL GHOSTBUSTERS™

Story **JOHN CARNELL** ⊘ Art **PHIL ELLIOTT** and **BAMBOS** ⊘ Lettering **BAMBOS** ⊘ Colouring **STUART PLACE**

Story **DAN ABNETT** ⊘ Art **TONY O'DONNELL** and **DAVE HARWOOD** ⊘ Colour **STEVE WHITE**

WINSTON'S DIARY

A DAY IN THE LIFE OF WINSTON ZEDDMORE

Wednesday, 12th July, 1989
Picture the scene. There was a cold wind whipping down off what Egon reliably informed me was 'The Trossachs'. Rain pelting down out of what Egon called 'a fine, glowing Caledonian sky' and mud from the banks of what Egon referred to as 'Loch Gloom', lapping over the tops of what I call 'my boots', making my feet something I generally refer to as 'wet and uncomfortable.'

It became clear at this point in our little expedition to the bleaker areas of Scotland, that Peter shared my outlook, because he began to refer to things in general as 'wet and uncomfortable.' Egon said he wished to remind Peter that McFrostie's book, *Buggaboos and Kelpie Folk of Kirkintilloch and Glen Bannockdoom*, indicated that our research was what he called 'vitally important to psychic investigation.' Ray added that finding a first edition of McFrostie's *Buggaboos and Kelpie Folk of Kirkintilloch and Glen Bannockdoom* in the second-hand shop in Mid Lothian, was what he would call 'a significant academic discovery.' Peter said that he thought anyone who wrote a book about Buggaboos and Kelpie Folk in places called Kirktintilloch

and Glen Bannockdoom was, in his opinion, something he generally described as 'mad as a pepperoni cheesecake.'

For something that I would call 'ten minutes' and Peter would call 'too long,' the two of us stood up to what we think of as 'our ankles', in what is regarded by many as 'thick mud', while Ray and Egon did something that they liked to think of as 'terribly useful' i.e. they stood around the banks of Loch Gloom taking PKE readings and generally looking up things in the by now soggy first edition of McFrostie's

Significant Academic Work about Buggaboos and whatnot.

After a while, I decided that it was probably worth taking an interest, because it would help take my mind off everything being 'wet and uncomfortable'. As far as I could make out, Ray and Egon had identified this particular part of the banks of Loch Gloom, as the site of the cursed *Castle Kelgrave*, the family seat of the ancient Scottish Clan, the McCloods of McClood, who had all perished in the terrible castle fire of Midwinter, 1487. Some said that this was because the McCloods of McClood had thrown one too many twigs on the fire that night in an effort to keep warm (The Midwinter of 1487 being particularly wet and uncomfortable even for the Trossachs), but there were quieter, bleaker rumours that the Clan McClood of McClood had offended some dark, primeval spirit of the Highlands and it had come blistering in on some keening, Caledonian gale that black night to |wreak terrible vengeance on the unfortunate Clan McClood of McClood.

"Since that time, according to McFrostie", said Egon, in what I call his 'serious voice', "strange things have haunted the banks of Loch Gloom here

in the dark Glen of Bannockdoom." "Buggaboos?" I asked. "Worse," said Ray. Ray and Egon shivered with what they call 'professional apprehension.' Peter and I shivered with what we call 'cold mud in our socks.'

So, we waited for what was by anyone's standard 'three or four hours' until night fell, wet and uncomfortable, about the banks of Loch Gloom. Then a certain amount of something 'Ghostbusters label – Bad Craziness' started to happen

Through the drizzle and mist in the night air, we made out the bleak and ghostly form of an ancient castle looming into being on the Glen slopes. "That", said Egon, "is what I call a spectral building." "Ulp", muttered Peter. Ghost or not, the castle looked solid

enough, and we aproached, through the damp thistles to the ancient gateway, chill winds tugged at us from the dark archway. A faint phantom glow shone from within, and we could all hear what was undoubtedly the wailing of spectral bagpipes, howling grimly from the depths of the spirit world, or at the very least, an especially wet and uncomfortable corner of the Trossachs.

Peter suggested that it might be a 'good idea' to stay outside for a while whilst we did a bit more background reading in McFrostie's *Doohickey Whatevers in Thingumy and Wherever*, but Ray and Egon had already disappeared into the dark gateway, so we hurried to catch up. Egon told us, in case we didn't know, that

we were in a phantom manifestation of Castle Kelgrave exactly as it had been on that fateful Midwinter in 1487 when the Clan McClood of McClood had met it's diabolical fate, and that this was an 'interesting thing.' Peter and I agreed that this would be an 'even more interesting thing' if thought about whilst relaxing somewhere dry and comfortable and miles away, like our Hotel in Inverness, or better still, Florida.

Peter had barely picked himself up off the floor, following the blow to the head with the copy of McFrostie that Ray had delivered, when we realised it was much too late to go back. Around and about us, phantom shapes were appearing. Sad, gloomy figures wrapped in long cloaks, shivering in a ghostly mass around a spectral fire that burned with a cold flame at the centre of the room. Egon whispered that these were the ghosts of the entire Clan McClood and this was another 'very interesting thing'. Peter asked Ray if he could borrow the book for a moment.

"Welcome yous strangers to the sad halls of the Clan McClood of McClood, you ken?" murmured the largest of the spooks, his long ectoplasmic beard in danger of falling in the grate.

"Thankyou", said Ray, brightly, "but my name's not Ken."

"No matter, laddie," answered the spook, turning his sad eyes towards us. "Yous all come here in a braw, dour night. A terrible sad time for the lost Clan McClood of McClood."

The other ghosts muttered "Aye aye" and wept and wailed a little about the terrible, sad night. At this point, Peter said he certainly agreed and it really was pretty terrible wasn't it?

The ghosts suddenly fell quiet and their leader went on "We'll no force yous to stay, but if ya can give us any help in this terrible, sad time, even a wee bit, we'd all be terrible grateful and ma wee son Jamie would compose a special reel in your honour."

One of the smaller spooks, who cradled a spidery bagpipe in his skeletal arms, sprang up eagerly, put the chanter to his lips and began pumping the bag, making a noise like a sackful of cats hitting a trampoline at high speed.

"Not yet, Jamie!" yelled the chief spook as the others cringed and clapped their hands over their ears. "Well, strangers, Yea or nay? Can yous help us?"

"Pardon?" asked Ray, who had Peter's hands over his ears (Peter had got terribly confused by this time).

"We'll help if we can." replied Egon. "What seems to be the Bad Craziness, sorry, the problem?"

"Why," muttered the spook, rolling his eyes, "Tis on this braw, wet moonless night that the foul monster of Loch Gloom rises above the oily waters and comes to Castle Kelgrave to warm his hide by our wee fire, you ken? But the tragedy of it is, the fire is too wee to warm him and the rest of us, and so in his wrath, he turns on us and destroys the castle and the whole of the Clan McClood of McClood!"

"About what time does

this usually happen?" asked Peter, but nobody heard him, for at that moment, there came a terrible wailing noise and a black, rubbery, fetid bulk lumbered out of the darkness into the glow of the wee fire. I mean small fire.

"Usually about now," answered the spook. The Monster was hideous and mishappen, his dark, shaggy coat dripping weed and filthy water onto the flagstones. He opened his dark maw and let out a bellow of fury and despair.

"Poor thing," said Ray, "he looks wet through."

"Too right, laddie!" barked the monster in a seal-like yelp. "I'm wet and uncomfortable and no mistake!"

"And," he added, leaning forward and fixing us with one dark and sinister eye, "unless I get a space by the fire tinight, there'll be the divil ta pay for the Clan McClood of McClood!"

At this, the Clan set to wailing and weeping again, and the Monster set to growling and moaning in a threatening way, and Peter did something Egon

later called 'Quite Wasteful', but which I tended to think of as probably the 'best thing to do in the circumstances.'

Once the fire was big enough to warm both the Clan McClood of McClood and the Monster of Loch Gloom, their happy spirits faded away along with the castle, never to trouble Glen Bannockdoom again.

We, of course, were left on the banks of the Loch in the middle of the night to trudge home to our Hotel feeling very wet and uncomfortable, but at least happy in the knowledge that another case was closed. Egon was the only one who was a little discontented. He reliably informed Peter that throwing McFrostie's *Buggaboos and Kelpie Folk of Kirkintilloch and Glen Bannockdoom* onto the fire to make it bigger, was a quite wasteful solution to a straight-forward, paranormal problem — four hundred and seventy-three times between Glen Bannockdoom and Inverness.

40

Dear Janine...
SO, THE GUYS WENT OFF AND LEFT ME HOLDING THE FORT... STILL, AT LEAST THEY HAD THE DECENCY TO SEND A CARD OR TWO!
Dear Janine,
Having a great time! They play some pretty mean sports here. I tried my hand at "Wellie Wangling" - it's not as easy as base-ball - I hit Peter on the head with my wellie - he was not amused. See you soon. love
Winston x
JANINE MELNITZ
GHOSTBUSTERS' HQ
NEW YORK
USA.

Some difficulty in getting spare parts for ECTO-1. The people are cute – such animal lovers. Do you know, they even have donkey sanctuaries.
Best Wishes,
Ray x.
P.S. Slimer wants to say hello –

Janine Melnitz
Ghostbusters' HQ.
New York.
U.S.A.

Hi, Janine,
Gee, thanks! Another great place you've sent us to – have you seen English weather? I mean, I should have packed my galoshes! Another thing – You didn't tell me Slimer was coming with us! And have you seen the food? Not a Twinkie in sight! Shucks! And when you said 'Holiday', you forgot to say 'Working Holiday'! Got to dash – I'm off to buy a present for Dana!   See Ya,
Peter xxx

Miss Janine Melnitz,
Ghostbusters' HQ.
The Big Apple.
U.S.A.

Janine,
Are you keeping an eye on my Fungi collection? Don't water the spores! This trip has been an ideal opportunity to acquire some of the rarer species of European Fungi, and to test out some of the new traps! I must take my leave – I've spotted a Stinkhorn – It's a fungus, Janine
Regards,
Egon.

Miss J. Melni...
GHOSTBUSTE...
NEW YO...

SPENGLER'S
SPIRIT GUIDE

The Spirit World, or Supercosmos, is a funny place. Certain areas of its multifacet dimensions are built upon principles of physics that are utterly different to those of our own cosmos. These pockets of Bad Craziness, or 'Singularities' as they are known, are the homes for some of the very biggest, most powerful, muckety-muck Demons there are.

The thing about this is, due to the alien-ness of their physical matrix, most of these demons find it very difficult to exist in our dimension for more than say, ooh, three or four seconds. Hence the creation and existence of the class six spooks known as the Servitor Races.

SERVITOR RACES

The most famous example of the Servitor Races, is one that became so well known that he got his face on the cover of *Newsweek* and made something of a hit in New York City. I speak, of course, of the giant Mr Stay-Puft Marshmallow Man. He demonstrates the principles of a Servitor precisely.

The process works like this: The class seven demon (in this case Gozer) observes our own dimension, and says to himself "Hmm, looks like a nice little world next door, one that I'd like to subjugate and so full of nice little bite-sized people . . . What a shame I can't just pop across inter-dimensionally and take over, but my ectoplasmic configuration would mean that I'd dissolve into my component atoms in say, ooh, three or four seconds.

I'm just guessing at what he'd say you understand. Anyway, instead, he sends across a lesser demonic entity (in this case Zuul) to scout around a bit, get the lie of the land and find out things like the price of spuds and who won Saturday's match. Then he launches his master plan by projecting his spirit, but not his body, into our dimension in a containing

form prepared by his lesser demon. In Gozer's case, Zuul made the containing form, or Servitor Race, in the shape of The Stay-Puft Marshmallow Man. Really, that was Ray's fault, he did that.

So, the Servitor is a recepticle, a puppet body through which the demon can operate in our dimension. In the case of Mr Stay-Puft, the Ghostbusters arrived in time and the rest, and Gozer, is history.

So, that's the principle behind it. Now a few specifics to demonstrate other instances of Servitor Races intruding into our dimension:

KWANINTHARNGII

The class seven, lordy-lordy king of everything. Kwanintharngii chose as his Servitor form, a giant cucumber. Nobody knows why. Kwanintharngii achieved little except win a prize at a fête.

DUJ

Duj was let down by his lesser demon, who didn't do his research thoroughly. Appearing in Florida in the form of a seventy-foot-high Neopolitan Ice-cream, he melted in say, ooh, three or four seconds.

THE REAL GH⊙STBUSTERS™

HAVE YOU GOT A ROOM FOR THE NIGHT, MA'AM?

YES, BUT I'VE ONLY GOT ROOM FOR *THREE* PEOPLE!

AFTER A LONG DAY'S JOURNEY...

BOY, I'M BUSHED. I COULD SLEEP *ANYWHERE!*

THIS LOOKS LIKE A GOOD PLACE TO STAY, WINSTON!

YEAH, *RAY,* AND FAR AWAY FROM THOSE SPOOKS!

CROWN I

SO ... JUST MY LUCK... THE *SHORT* STRAW. I'LL SLEEP IN *ECTO-1!*

SORRY, NO *PETS* ALLOWED!

OKAY, *PETER,* BUT IT LOOKS LIKE *SLIMER* WILL HAVE TO SLEEP WITH *YOU!*

OH NO... HE PROBABLY *SNORES* AS WELL AS *SLIMES!*

GOBBLECHOMP NIGHTYNIGHT PETEY WEETYCHOMPCHOMP!

THIS IS LIKE SLEEPING IN A *DUSTBIN!*

Story JOHN CARNELL ⊘ Art DOUGIE BRAITHWAITE and DAVE HARWOOD ⊘ Lettering HEL ⊘ Colouring CHRIS MATTHEWS

Story **JOHN FREEMAN** ⊘ Art **ANDY WILDMAN** and **DAVE HARWOOD** ⊘ Colour **STEVE WHITE**

THE DEMON BOWLER!

I t was early evening when the trouble began again. Another haunting in the Twentieth Century with all its problems, we could have done well without. As darkness crept over the city, and the lights came on in the streets, the sky scrapers and suburban houses, the whole metropolis seemed to catch its breath, as if waiting for something to happen.

Outside *Big Al's Big Bowling Alley* in downtown New York, a cold, icy wind suddenly whipped up from nowhere, sending litter and leaves spiralling down the almost deserted street. "Strange", thought a street tramp, buttoning his old, tattered coat, as he noticed how odd the weather had become for mid-July. Hadn't he been sunbathing in Central Park only yesterday?

Without warning, unseen forces grabbed him and he yelped in surprise and fear. The invisible force spun him round and wicked, hysterical laughter cut the air like a knife. "A game, a game! This is the place!" came a ghostly cry. "It's been so looooong!" The tramp was pushed harshly to the ground by unseen hands, as paper and leaves scurried towards the doors of the bowling alley. The doors swung open, then slammed shut just as suddenly. The wind dropped. From inside the bowling alley, there were screams of terror, flickers of blinding colour, then silence.

The tramp jumped up, grabbed his fallen, battered hat and ran for his life, not looking back once. He'd seen some strange things in his time, but nothing like this!

"Strike! Well done, Janine!"

Inside *Big Al's*, a few days later, the Ghostbusters' secretary turned away from the bowling lane as all the pins fell to her well-aimed bowl, a look of triumph on her face. "Another game, anyone?" All four Ghostbusters – Peter, Winston, Ray and Egon – looked at each other dubiously, having already been beaten by Janine three times in a row. "Ah . . . Perhaps a game of checkers?", suggested Peter. Janine's bowling skills had been quite unexpected. They'd all underestimated her yet again.

"Oh come on, you guys! I was just getting warmed up!"

Janine reached for her diet cola and looked around the large bowling alley for another victim. It was a large, brightly-lit place, painted in brash red and yellow, looking as clean and new as the day it had been opened, in the days when bowling was the sport to be played. A jukebox played Motown hits quietly in the background, and the long bowling lanes were clean, the skittles in place waiting for a game, but apart from the Ghostbusters, there was no-one else around, only the barman.

"This place sure is empty for a Saturday night," Janine commented. Ray and Winston looked strangely nervous. "I thought we would have to wait ages for a game." Egon suddenly looked guilty, as if he'd rather be anywhere than under Janine's gaze just then.

The temperature suddenly dropped. "There's, um, a perfectly illogical, paranormal reason for the absence of patrons, Janine." Egon muttered, in a voice he usually reserved for talking to his spore collection.

"There sssssscertainly is", said a disembodied, grating voice. "Me!"

Peter shrieked as blue ecto-slime appeared from nowhere and poured down his face. Ray was thrown against Winston by an unseen force, then the two of them were spun on the polished floor like a pair of hopelessly uncoordinated breakdancers. In the nearby bar, every bottle of beer burst open, sending brown liquid spattering to the ceiling. With a cry of dismay, the bar steward, threw his cleaning towel to the floor and ran hurriedly for the nearest exit. Unseen forces grabbed him, spun him round, giggling, and threw him out of the doors.

"What is it?", shouted Janine.

"I'm not sure", replied Winston, "but I don't think it's here to apply for the job of bouncer!"

Wind twisted round the Ghostbusters, and Egon and Janine fought to stand up, grabbing each other for support. A horrid looking, long-armed manifestation slipped and slinked into existence, leaving the alley thick with the pervasive smell of sulphur. The creature cackled furiously, exposing its sharp, pointed teeth which gleamed in the bright lights of the bowling alley. It had a bowling ball bag in its right hand and wore enormous bowling shoes.

Egon quickly stepped away from Janine, embarrassed. Janine was disappointed. "Ah, you must be the Demon Bowler", he said, peering inquisitively at the giggling creature. He knew full well that if he had a PKE Meter on him right now, the readings would have been well off all known scales.

"I sssssscertainly am!", said the demon. "Then do you know my humble challenge, humans?"

"Don't tell me, it's something along the lines of the 'Play - me - and - save - your-life' routine, isn't it?", Ray put in, as he struggled to disentangle himself from Winston. Peter was staggering around, wincing and trying to remove the ectoplasm from his left ear, without much success.

"Correct!", replied the cackling ghost. "Not that knowing the challenge will help, you pathetic creatures. If you defeat me, I will leave this place forever. If you lose . . . you have to play bowls with me FOREVER!"

The demon jangled a strange bag strapped to its belt from which some terrible wails emerged. "I warn you, mortals, no-one has EVER beaten me! I have built up QUITE a collection!"

Janine stepped forward, before any of the Ghostbusters could stop her. She jabbed defiantly at the pompous demon with her long, manicured finger. "I'll play you", she hissed. "You're NOT going to ruin the only evening out I've had for weeks!"

The demon laughed its horrible laugh once more, and snapped his fingers. At the end of the bowling lane a strange set of bowling pins suddenly appeared. They were shaped like brooding devils, wings folded, brows furrowed and looked almost alive! The temperature seemed to drop once more. "Let us begin ", grinned the demon. "I alwaaaaays enjoy an easy game!"

The ghost began to warm up, swinging its bowling ball around its head, dancing up and down at the end of the lane and laughing horribly. Putting a finger to his lips, urging quiet, Peter took Janine to one side. "Keep him playing, whatever you do", he whispered, "I'm sorry to have tricked you into coming here". "Not as sorry as you're going to be!", Janine cut in. "I should have known this was another of your undercover busts! When was the last time you guys offered to take me out for the evening?"

"Please, Janine", whispered Egon, desperately. "We have to get rid of this ghost for the owner, but we must rescue the victims

he's carrying in that bag, too. It's not a straightfoward bust". "I'm waaaaaaaiting!" shrieked the ghost.

Janine smiled at Egon, still smarting. "I'm ready", she said, turning back to the bowling lane. "Ladies first, I think!" Adjusting her glasses, Janine took careful aim at the strange bowling pins, then swung the ball and with a deft flick, she sent it careering down the lane. It looked set for a full strike and Janine smiled smugly, but at the last moment, the pins jumped out of the ball's path. "Hey!" shouted Janine. "What's going on?"

The ghost giggled. The bowling pins at the end of the lane fell about laughing, sprouting arms to hold their sides.

"Just a little joke of mine", said the ghost.

"Well, you play fair or not at all", shouted Janine. "You don't seriously think that I'm going to play with a cheat, do you?"

"Oh, very well!", muttered the ghost, looking disappointed. "You humans take threats of eternal torture so seriously". As the ghost reset the pins with another click of its fingers, it didn't notice that Peter had slipped quietly away during the argument.

The Ghostbusters watched with some amusement, as Janine scored strike after strike, knocking all the pins down in one bowl. Having decided not to cheat, the ghost was now regretting its decision, but it had its pride and was no pushover either. "I haven't been bowling for a thousand years to be beaten by the likes of you", it snapped. Janine noticed that Peter

had returned, clean again and with a Proton Gun hidden under his jacket.

"Perhaps that bag on your belt is affecting your bowling?", suggested Janine. "Throwing you off balance? It's so easily done."

"Yes, that's it, of course!" The ghost removed the bag and prepared for its final throw. It took its usual run up and then let go of its ebony bowling bowl. The ball went flying down the lane, wobbled, dribbled, then missed the skittles completely. The Demon Bowler, demon no longer, gave a howl of despair that cut right through the flesh to the very bone.

Janine grabbed the bag and threw it to Egon before the bowler could have second thoughts on the deal. Peter stepped out, pushed a Ghost Trap under the ghost and raised his Proton Gun.

"You've played your last match, spook!", he said, depressing the release button on his cannon. The ghost

turned, wailed and then vanished into the Trap. Egon dropped the bag with a start, as it changed shape to release its captured victims. People of many ages, in period costume emerged rubbing their eyes in astonishment, confused at the bright lights and the strange appearance of their rescuers.

Janine turned to the Ghostbusters, hands on hips and looking very stern. "Before this place gets crowded, I believe you owe me a very big, very expensive meal in the very best restaurant in town!"

"Hey guys", said Peter turning to the others, "wasn't there a restaurant bust that needed the subtle approach, too? *Berghoffs* in Chicago, wasn't it?"

"Under the circumstances", replied Winston, grinning as he thought of their own, ever-hungry ghost-friend that they'd left back at HQ. "I think we'd better send Slimer to deal with that one!"

MAKE YOUR OWN

SLIMER!

To make your very own Slimer glove-puppet, you will need:
Two pieces of green felt (approx. 18 cm square), A piece of pink felt (approx. 14 cm x 16 cm), Some pieces of pink, red and yellow felt for the features, A pair of round-ended scissors, Tracing paper, A pencil, A needle and thread, Fabric Glue.

To make up your puppet:
1. Trace the pattern pieces off the page opposite using the tracing paper and cut them out of your felt pieces. (You will need to cut two of the basic Slimer shapes.)
2. Glue all of the features apart from the pink tongue onto one piece of the green felt.
3. Fold the tongue in half and stitch the centre to the bottom of the mouth.
4. Join the two sides of the tongue either with glue or with thread.
5. You are now ready to sew the pieces of green felt together. Don't forget to leave the bottom of your puppet open, so you can put your hand inside.

Congratulations! Now you have your very own Slimer! One word of warning – Keep him away from the fridge!

(attach tongue here)

(do not sew along this line)

(fold here)

IN THE TOWER OF LONDON SLIMER IS SEARCHING FOR SOMETHING...

DO NOT FEED THE RAVENS

CAW!

NOPE-A-DOPE, NOTTY HERE!

SILLYBILLYS NOTS IN HERE NEITHER!

THE CROWN JEWELS HANDS OFF!

YIPPEEYAHOOEE! THEY THERE IS!

SLIMER WANT TO BE BEEFYEATER AS WELL! YUM YUMMY YUM!

EEEK

AAGGH!

Story **BAMBOS** ⊘ Art and Lettering **BAMBOS** ⊘ Colouring **HEL**

THE REAL GHOSTBUSTERS™

Story **JOHN CARNELL** ⊘ Art **JOHN GEERING** and **DAVE HARWOOD** ⊘ Lettering **HEL** ⊘ Colouring **EUAN PETERS**

54

55

THE REAL GH⊙STBUSTERS™

Story JOHN CARNELL ⊘ **Art ANTHONY LARCOMBE** ⊘ **Lettering GLIB** ⊘ **Colouring STEVE WHITE**

61